Thanks to my son Leo, the
inspiration of many dreams,
to my wife Barbara, for her
tenacity.

Thanks to my mum and dad
for making me a dreamer,
to my sister for keeping
my feet on the ground.

Thanks to Felicia, Rhian and
Virginia for believing in me.

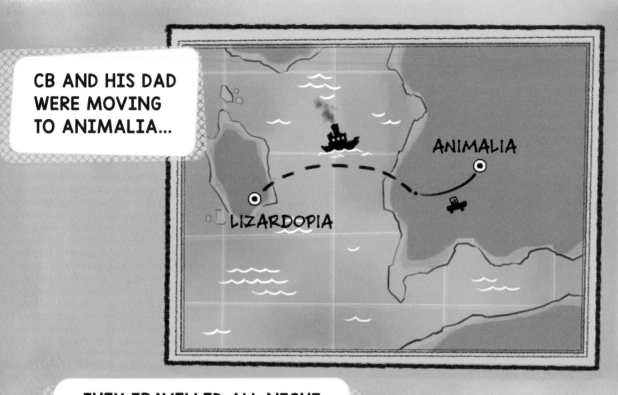

CB AND HIS DAD WERE MOVING TO ANIMALIA...

... THEY TRAVELLED ALL NIGHT...

EVEN CB'S
FAVOURITE
COMIC BOOK
FED HIS DREAD...

THEY ARRIVED AT SCHOOL...

Have a great day CB!

 Uggghh!

Be strong. It will all be fine.

This is going to be the worst day of my life

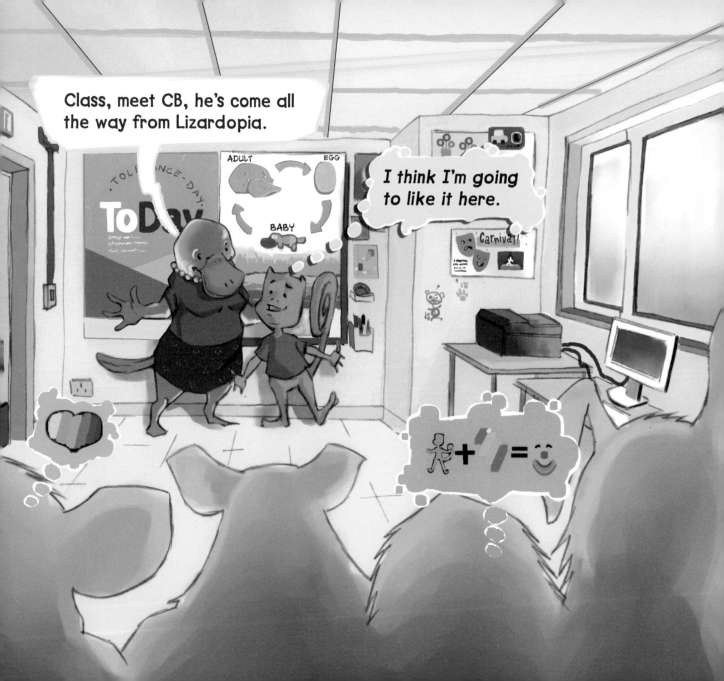

AFTER ALL, ONCE YOU GOT TO KNOW THEM...

...HOW COULD YOU NOT LOVE THESE GUYS?

THE END

SECRET SECTiON (for kids only)

We are all scared sometimes. It is useful to be afraid of things that could harm us - such as poisonous snakes or fast-moving cars – but there are some fears that can end up holding us back.

Think of it like this: you start out life with a large open swimming pool with lots of space and you swim everywhere. Then you think you see a poop in one corner and you say, "I'm not swimming over there any more". Then you think you see another poop, so you avoid swimming in that other corner. Eventually you end up thinking there is poop everywhere, and swimming in only a tiny patch of water.

And that's what life would be like if you let fear stop you from exploring and discovering.

If there were real poops in the pool you might want to wait until they were taken out and it was cleaned – but you shouldn't stop swimming in that fine pool!

What are you scared of? Use this space to draw or write it down.

Colour this in relaxed happy colours.

Colour this one in scared, angry colours.

Can you spot the 8 differences?

In case you were interested...

Scientists have recently discovered that chameleons change colour by adjusting a layer of special cells, composed of nanocrystals of different size, shape and organisation nestled within their skin. Changing the structure of these crystals affects how light reflects off their skin...amazing!

Some people think that they do this to camouflage themselves against a background. In fact, chameleons mostly change colour to change their temperatures or to warn other chameleons.

Only adult male chameleons change colour, especially when they see a rival male chameleon they want to chase away, or a female to attract. Females and young chameleons are dull-coloured. In this book we played with reality a bit and made CB change colour so he can show us how he's feeling.

my big

sister

by Valorie Fisher

POCKET BOOKS

LONDON

ACKNOWLEDGMENTS

I am immensely grateful to Elinor Hills for her hard work, gracious smile, and delightful scowl. I would like to thank my son, Aidan, for being the perfect photographer's assistant and for lending me Bullet, Brooklyn's fastest goldfish; Bernadette Frishberg, a most expressive baby; Isadora and Miles Schappell-Spillman, whose Frances Popcorn was a lovely guinea pig of enormous talent; my mother, Susan Fisher, a rodent milliner extraordinaire; Mia and Romy Faucher-Mayhew for their much-too-much-loved dolls; and my brother, Kevin Fisher, for his insight into sisters, big and little. And I am deeply grateful for the continued support, enthusiasm, and friendship of Lee Wade and Anne Schwartz.

POCKET
BOOKS

First published in Great Britain in 2004 by Pocket Books,
an imprint of Simon & Schuster UK Ltd
Africa House, 64-78 Kingsway, London WC2B 6AH

Originally published in 2003 by Atheneum Books for Young Readers, an
imprint of Simon & Schuster Children's Publishing Division, New York.

Copyright © 2003 by Valorie Fisher

A CIP catalogue record for this book is available from the
British Library upon request

Book design by Lee Wade
The text for this book was set in Filosophia

ISBN 0743478193

Printed in China

1 3 5 7 9 10 8 6 4 2

For Mum and Dad

This is my
big sister.

It's hard for me to keep up with her.

She takes very good care of me,

except when
she leaves me
with the neighbour.

She likes to pick out
everyone's clothes.

My big sister
kisses me,

and sometimes
she doesn't.

If I'm good,
she takes me
to the zoo

or introduces me
to her friends.

But I'm not supposed to bother her when she's working.

Animal training takes up a lot of her time.

My big sister
gets oodles of
phone calls;

sometimes she lets me talk too.

I love my
big sister,

and she loves me.